GRAPHIC PREHISTORIC ANIMALS

MEGA SHARK

MEGALODON

ILLUSTRATED BY ALESSANDRO POLUZZI

COLOURED BY OLIVER WEST

FRANKLIN WATTS

LONDON•SYDNEY

Franklin Watts
This edition published in the UK in 2018 by The Watts Publishing Group

Designed and illustrated by David West

ISBN 9781445159102 (hardback)
ISBN 9781445159119 (paperback)

Printed in Malaysia

Franklin Watts
An imprint of
Hachette Children's Group
Part of The Watts Publishing Group
Carmelite House
50 Victoria Embankment
London EC4Y 0DZ

An Hachette UK company.
www.hachette.co.uk

www.franklinwatts.co.uk

GRAPHIC PREHISTORIC ANIMALS MEGA SHARK
was produced for Franklin Watts by
David West Children's Books, 6 Princeton Court, 55 Felsham Road, London SW15 1AZ

CONTENTS

WHAT IS A MEGA SHARK?
Learn the facts about this amazing animal.
page 4

THE STORY...
MEGA SHARK IN THE PACIFIC OCEAN
page 6

FOSSIL FINDS
Find out about amazing mega shark fossils.
page 22

ANIMAL GALLERY
Look up the animals that appear in the story.
page 23

GLOSSARY AND INDEX
page 24

Words in **bold** can be found in the glossary.

WHAT IS A MEGA SHARK?

MEGALODON MEANS 'BIG TOOTH'

Megalodons lived around 16 million to 1.6 million years ago, during the **Miocene** and **Pliocene periods**. **Fossils** of their remains have been found all around the world (see page 22).

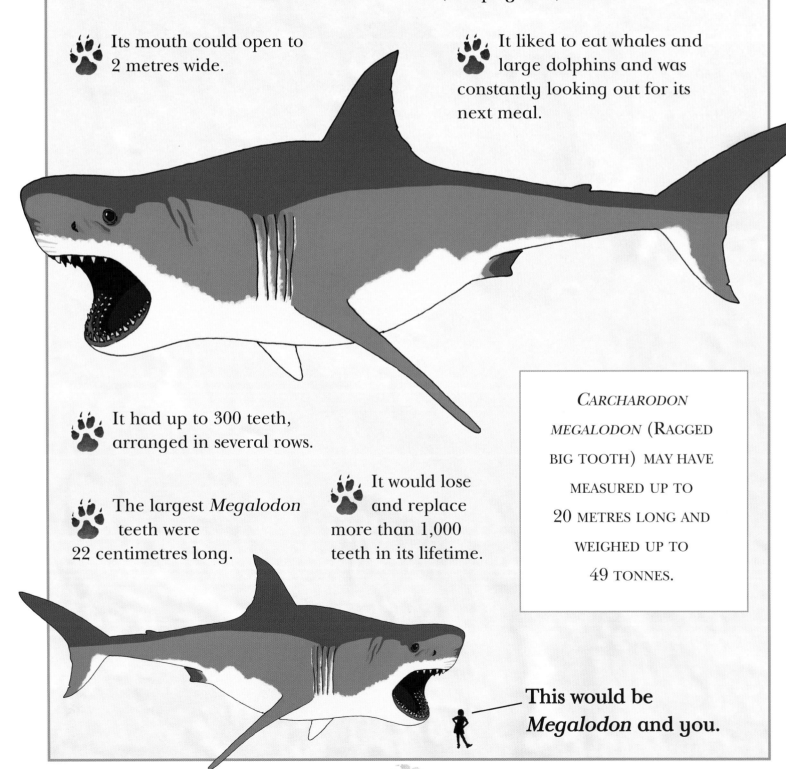

Its mouth could open to 2 metres wide.

It liked to eat whales and large dolphins and was constantly looking out for its next meal.

It had up to 300 teeth, arranged in several rows.

The largest *Megalodon* teeth were 22 centimetres long.

It would lose and replace more than 1,000 teeth in its lifetime.

CARCHARODON MEGALODON (RAGGED BIG TOOTH) MAY HAVE MEASURED UP TO 20 METRES LONG AND WEIGHED UP TO 49 TONNES.

This would be *Megalodon* and you.

Judging by the size and shape of its teeth, scientists believe *Megalodon* would have looked like a giant-sized great white shark. Like the great white, the mega shark had rows of **serrated** teeth. They could saw through flesh and bone like a steak knife. Mega shark would also have had a modern shark's hunting senses – a powerful sense of smell and the ability to detect tiny electrical signals from mammals' heartbeats and fishes' gills.

Equipped with a slippery torpedo-like body and large fins and tail, *Megalodon* would have closed in and struck at its prey with the speed and surprise of a fast-attack submarine.

The great white shark's favourite food is seal – easy to catch and with a blubbery body that provides maximum energy. *Megalodon* hunted whales for the same reasons and could sense a **pod** from 3.2 kilometres away.

A great white shark tooth is only 6 centimetres long – the Megalodon's is 18 centimetres. The great white (below) is the largest modern-day predatory fish, but it would have been prey among mega sharks.

MEGA SHARK IN THE PACIFIC OCEAN

SUMMERTIME, FOUR MILLION YEARS AGO, OFF THE COAST OF WHAT IS NOW PERU.

TWO LARGE SHARKS ARE BORN FROM A MONSTER MOTHER – A FULL-GROWN MEGALODON – IN THE SHALLOW COASTAL WATERS THAT WILL BE THEIR NURSERY.

ONCE FREE, THE BABY SHARKS SWIM AWAY AS FAST AS POSSIBLE TO AVOID BEING EATEN BY THEIR MOTHER.

AS THEY HEAD TOWARDS THE REEF, A SHADOW PASSES OVERHEAD. IT IS A LONG-FINNED MAKO SHARK, ATTRACTED BY THE SCENT OF THE BIRTH.

BUT THE MAKO IS NOT MUCH BIGGER THAN THE BABIES AND CRUISES PAST. THE BABIES SWIM ALONG THE CORAL LOOKING FOR FOOD.

THREE YEARS LATER ONLY ONE OF THE BABIES IS STILL ALIVE. THE SURVIVING SHARK, A MALE, HAS GROWN TO 2.9 METRES LONG, AND IS ON THE HUNT FOR PREY.

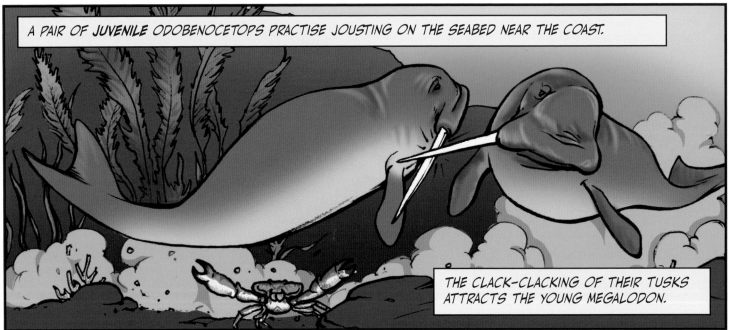

A PAIR OF **JUVENILE** ODOBENOCETOPS PRACTISE JOUSTING ON THE SEABED NEAR THE COAST.

THE CLACK-CLACKING OF THEIR TUSKS ATTRACTS THE YOUNG MEGALODON.

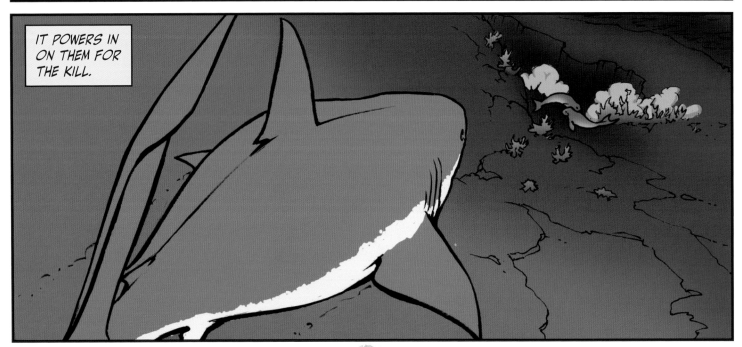

IT POWERS IN ON THEM FOR THE KILL.

THE ODOBENOCETOPS SPOT THE MEGALODON JUST IN TIME.

THEY SWIM AWAY, USING THEIR TUSKS TO WHIP UP CLOUDS OF **SEDIMENT** FROM THE SEABED TO HIDE THEMSELVES.

THE YOUNG SHARK VEERS PAST A FEEDING THALASSOCNUS. THE SEA SLOTH REMAINS MOTIONLESS UNTIL THE SHARK PASSES.

THE MEGALODON SEES A POD OF DWARF KILLER WHALES HEADING INSHORE. THE POD MIGHT MISTAKE IT FOR A MEAL.

A GROUP OF ACROPHOCA ARE ALSO OUT HUNTING TODAY. THEY CLOSE IN ON A SHOAL OF HERRING.

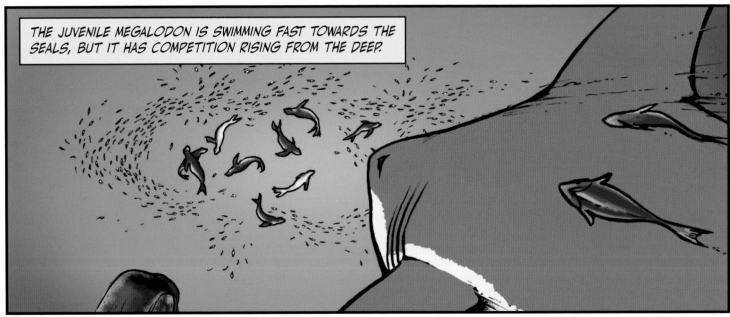

THE JUVENILE MEGALODON IS SWIMMING FAST TOWARDS THE SEALS, BUT IT HAS COMPETITION RISING FROM THE DEEP.

IT IS A JUVENILE *RAPTORIAL SPERM WHALE.*

THE SPERM WHALE APPROACHES THE MEGALODON AND USES ITS BULK TO BUMP THE SHARK ASIDE.

THE MEGALODON TWISTS TO SNAP AT THE SPERM WHALE, BUT THE WHALE HAS ALREADY SHOT FORWARDS IN A FLURRY OF BUBBLES.

THE ACROPHOCA SPOT THE DANGER AND DART AWAY FROM THE HERRING TO HEAD FOR SHORE.

THE SEALS SWIM QUICKLY TO SHORE AND BEGIN TO LEAP FROM THE WATER.

THE SPERM WHALE IS RELUCTANT TO ENTER THE SHALLOW WATER AND RISK GETTING STUCK. IT TURNS AWAY.

BUT OTHER HUNTERS ARE NOT SO CAREFUL.

ON THE BEACH A DWARF KILLER WHALE RIDES THE SURF INTO SHORE ON ITS BELLY...

...AND GETS ITS BREAKFAST.

TWELVE YEARS LATER THE MALE MEGALODON IS FULLY GROWN. IT IS BY FAR THE LARGEST PREDATOR TO STALK THE OCEAN.

IT IS AN HOUR AFTER DAWN – ITS BEST HUNTING TIME – WHEN THE WATER IS STILL DIM AND MURKY FROM THE NIGHT-TIME.

A POD OF PORPOISES GIVE THE GIANT A WIDE BERTH AS THEY PASS, BUT MEGALODON IS LOOKING FOR BIGGER GAME TO FEED ITS GIGANTIC APPETITE.

CRUISING THE SURFACE, IT SENSES THAT A POD OF CETOTHERIUMS IS GATHERED SOME DISTANCE AWAY. AN ALBATROSS AND GULLS CIRCLE ITS FIN, WAITING FOR SCRAPS.

THE MIGHTY MEGALODON BEGINS TO DIVE, SCARING OFF A GREAT WHITE SHARK THAT HAS BEEN CHASING A PORPOISE.

MEGALODON'S DARK GREY UPPER BODY BLENDS INTO THE MURKY GLOOM AS IT DESCENDS.

THE CETOTHERIUMS ARE BUSY FEEDING ON A RICH SHOAL OF **KRILL** THAT HAS RISEN TO THE SURFACE. THEY ARE UNAWARE OF THE DISTANT DIVING SHARK.

JUST ABOVE THE OCEAN FLOOR THE MEGALODON LEVELS OFF AND POSITIONS ITSELF FOR AN ATTACK RUN. IT DISTURBS THE STINGRAYS AND THE HAMMERHEAD SHARK THAT WAS HUNTING THEM.

PROPELLING ITSELF STRAIGHT UPWARDS WITH EVER-FASTER FLICKS OF ITS IMMENSE AND POWERFUL TAIL, THE MEGALODON LEAVES SHARKS AND TURTLES TOSSED IN ITS WAKE.

GATHERING SPEED, THE MEGALODON AIMS STRAIGHT AT THE POD ON THE SURFACE.

THE SHARK'S UPWARDS ANGLE CLOAKS IT FROM THE CETOTHERIUMS' ECHOLOCATION.

AND EVEN IF THEY DO SEE IT, THERE IS NOWHERE TO RUN.

MANTA RAYS SWERVE TO AVOID THE RISING SHARK.

THE SHARK REACHES **TERMINAL VELOCITY**, MOUTH WIDE OPEN.

IT IS HONING IN ON A JUVENILE CETOTHERIUM WHICH IT CAN KILL WITH ONE BITE AND EAT QUICKLY.

THE MEGALODON **BREACHES**, LIFTING THE JUVENILE OUT OF THE WATER AND BALANCING IT ON ITS NOSE A MOMENT.

BUT THE SHARK MISJUDGED THE WEIGHT. THE WHALE TOPPLES OVER ITS HEAD TO LAND BACK INTO THE SEA.

THE MEGALODON TURNS AROUND TO ATTACK AGAIN BUT QUICK CHANGES OF DIRECTION ARE DIFFICULT WITH SUCH A MASSIVE BODY.

THE DELAY GIVES THE POD A CHANCE TO ESCAPE.

THE MEGALODON STARTS TO CHASE THEM, BUT THE WHALES ARE USED TO SWIMMING LONG DISTANCES.

FINALLY, AN ELDERLY CETOTHERIUM'S STRENGTH GIVES OUT. IT PEELS OFF TO DIVE AND SEEK REFUGE IN THE DEEP.

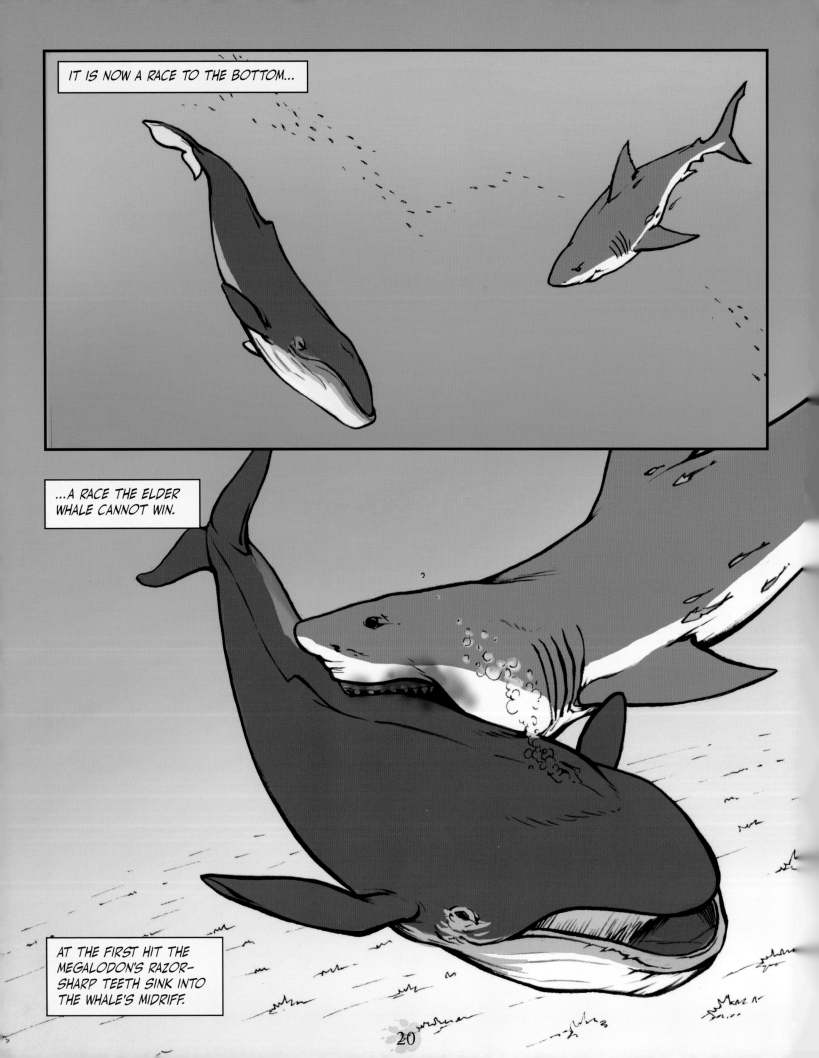

IT IS NOW A RACE TO THE BOTTOM...

...A RACE THE ELDER WHALE CANNOT WIN.

AT THE FIRST HIT THE MEGALODON'S RAZOR-SHARP TEETH SINK INTO THE WHALE'S MIDRIFF.

THE SHARK THRASHES ITS HEAD FROM SIDE TO SIDE TO SLICE OFF A HUNK OF FLESH. IT LOSES SOME TEETH IN THE PROCESS.

IT GRABS ITS MOUTHFUL AND SWIMS AWAY TO SWALLOW IT, LEAVING THE DOOMED CETOTHERIUM TO DRIFT IN SHOCK.

THE KILL QUICKLY ATTRACTS OTHER PREDATORS OF ALL SIZES, READY TO FEED.

BUT THEY ALL MAKE WAY FOR THE MEGALODON AS IT SWIMS BACK FOR ANOTHER BITE.

FOSSIL FINDS

WE CAN GET A GOOD IDEA OF WHAT **ANCIENT ANIMALS** MAY HAVE LOOKED LIKE FROM THEIR FOSSILS. FOSSILS ARE FORMED WHEN THE HARD PARTS OF AN ANIMAL OR PLANT BECOME BURIED AND THEN TURN TO ROCK OVER MILLIONS OF YEARS.

Fossilised Megalodon

teeth have been unearthed since medieval times. Then they were thought to be the tongues of dragons and giant snakes turned to stone.

Apart from a small section of spine, no piece of a Megalodon skeleton has ever been discovered.

Shark skeletons

are made from cartilage, which is softer than bone and rarely fossilises. The thousands of *Megalodon* teeth discovered are their only remains and the basis of their reconstruction.

Megalodon ruled

the greater part of the world's oceans for 14 million years, dying out just before the first great ice age. A combination of shrinking seas (bound up in ice at the poles), the disappearance of warm water whales (its food source), and the drying out of coastal waters (its nurseries) doomed the mega shark.

Reconstructions of Megalodon jaws in museums around the world are based on the various sizes of found fossil teeth. Even the smallest jaw is wide enough to swallow a man whole.

ANIMAL GALLERY

All of these **animals** appear in the story.

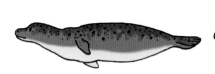

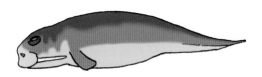

Acrophoca
'extreme seal'
Length: 1.5 metres
A primitive seal that had a long neck and short flippers and could not swim as well as modern seals.

Thalassocnus
'sea sloth'
Length: 1.8 metres
A bizarre, sloth-like creature that anchored itself to the seabed to graze on reeds.

Odobenocetops
'walrus-face whale'
Length: 2.1 metres
A cross between a walrus and a manatee that had a long right tusk and a short left one.

dwarf killer whale
Orcinus citoniensis
Length: 4 metres
Very similar to a small modern killer whale but with a few extra teeth, it hunted in packs.

great white shark
Carcharodon carcharias
Average length: 4.6 metres
The great white shared the prehistoric oceans with Megalodon and survived to modern times by adapting to life in colder waters.

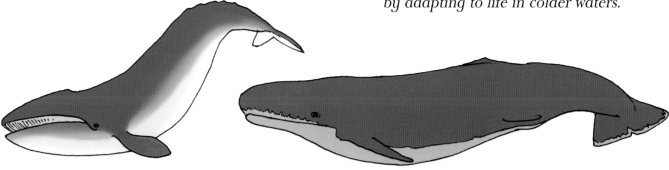

Cetotherium
'whale beast'
Length: 14.6 metres
An ancient **baleen whale**, like a smaller, sleeker grey whale, that used plates of whalebone to sift water for krill and small marine animals.

raptorial sperm whale
Length: 6 metres
A predatory physeter (blow pipe) whale that differed from modern sperm whales by having teeth in the upper as well as lower jaw.

GLOSSARY

baleen whale a whale that has whalebone plate 'teeth' to sift plankton

breach to break clear of the water

echolocation the locating of objects by using reflected sound, as practised by whales, dolphins and bats

fossil the remains of a living thing which have turned to rock

juvenile a young animal not yet fully grown

krill shrimp-like plankton (microscopic organisms that drift in the sea)

Miocene period time between 23 million to 5 million years ago when grasslands slowly replaced Earth's great forests

Pliocene period time between 5 million and 2 million years ago just before the start of the ice ages

pod a group of whales or dolphins

predator an animal that preys on others

raptorial grabbing

sediment matter that settles to the bottom of the sea

serrated having a jagged, saw-like edge

terminal velocity maximum achievable speed

INDEX

Acrophocas, 10, 11, 23
albatrosses, 14

Cetotheriums, 14, 15, 18, 19, 23

dolphins, 4
dwarf killer whales, 9, 12, 23

great white sharks, 5, 14, 23

hammerhead sharks, 16

krill, 15

mako sharks, 7
manta rays, 17

Odobenocetops, 8, 9, 23

pods, 5, 9, 13, 17, 19

porpoises, 13, 14

raptorial sperm whales, 10, 23

seals, 5, 10, 12, 23
sperm whales, 10, 11, 12, 23
stingrays, 16

Thalassocnuses, 9, 23
turtles, 16